Stephen Greenhorn was born in West Lothian, Scotland in 1964 and started writing professionally in 1989 while still at university. Greenhorn's work has been produced by a wide variety of theatre companies across the UK – including community groups and children's theatre companies – as well as on radio and television.

Notable successes include *The Salt Wound* (1994) for 7:84 Theatre Company and *Passing Places* (1997) for the Traverse Theatre, Edinburgh. In 1998 he collaborated on *Sleeping Around* for Paines Plough Theatre Company in London, and returned to 7:84 to produce *Dissent*. In the same year, the published script of *Passing Places* earned him a place on the shortlist of the Stakis Prize for Scottish Writer of the Year.

Most recently, he has adapted *King Matt* (2001/2003) for TAG Theatre Company, translated *The Ballad of Crazy Paola* (2001) for the Traverse and collaborated on *Gilt* (2003) for 7:84. For TV he has written episodes of *The Bill* and *Where the Heart Is* and his own six-part drama series *Glasgow Kiss* was screened by BBC 1. In 2002 he created *River City*, a new soap opera, for BBC Scotland.

He is currently working on several projects for film, television and theatre. He lives in Glasgow.

Capercaillie Books

King Matt
by Stephen Greenhorn

adapted from the book
King Matt The First
by Janusz Korczak

Capercaillie Books

CAPERCAILLIE BOOKS LIMITED

Published by Capercaillie Books Limited,

Registered Office 48 North Castle Street, Edinburgh.

Design by Ian Kirkwood Design.

Printed in Great Britain by Antony Rowe Ltd, Chippenham, Wiltshire.

Set in Cosmos and Veljovic

A catalogue record for this book is available from the British Library
ISBN 0-9545206-2-9.

The publisher acknowledges support from the Scottish Arts Council towards the publication of this title.

For Zack. The most Matt-like boy I know

Introduction

When TAG Theatre Company first approached me about adapting a children's book for the stage I was wary. Adaptations are strange beasts. They are so difficult to get right that an immense degree of enthusiasm is required before taking them on. When TAG explained that the book in question was an out-of-print Polish classic from the 1920's my suspicions increased. When they handed me a dog-eared copy of an old American translation my heart sank. And then I read it . . .

King Matt the First is an astonishing book. On one level it is simply a fantastic roller-coaster adventure story about an eleven-year-old boy who becomes a king. What makes it so special, however, is the the way Janusz Korczak merges the world of childhood with the complex realities of adult life. He never shies away from confronting Matt with the truth about how surprising, painful and confusing the world can be. Matt experiences war, politics, diplomacy and democracy and each is presented 'warts and all'. There is no condescension, no simple escapism.

Korczak was a children's doctor in turn-of-the-century Poland who also saw service in the military. His radical ideas about the empowerment and development of children were years ahead of his time. No plain theorist, he put his ideas into practice when he ran his own orphanage in Warsaw. It became a mini-republic for children, with its own parliament, court and newspaper. Much of this experience is reflected in the story of King Matt.

When the book was published it became a treasured piece of children's literature throughout Eastern Europe. It is still held in the same kind of affection and regard as, say, *Alice in*

Wonderland or *Peter Pan* are in this country. Like these, it is a work which can be enjoyed by all ages. It has something important to say about the place of children in society, about the way adults treat them, about the responsibilities they are given and those they are denied. However, all of this is explored in a story which is breathtakingly paced and both funny and heartbreaking in turn.

As you may have guessed, I too fell under the spell of this remarkable tale and could not resist the challenge of trying to bring it to the stage. Having agreed, however, I began to realise the enormity of the task. Amongst other things, *King Matt the First* involves numerous battles, several long journeys, parliamentary debates, riots, explosions and parades. The most difficult and brutal part of the process was the editing down of the material and the choices about which sections to focus on. I tried to do this on a thematic basis rather than worry about the practical problems of staging certain incidents. I knew we would only have a handful of actors to work with but was determined to keep a sense of the epic sweep of the story. In the end, even having decided to leave out the plane crash, the wolf hunt and the jungle expedition, I knew there were going to have to be some imaginative theatrical solutions!

In the end I relied on the astounding versatility of the cast and created a kind of Greek chorus of narrators who would shift in and out of character around the central figure of Matt. I also decided to write the narrative sections in rhyme, partly to distinguish it from the dramatic dialogue and partly because it was fun. The chorus element also allowed a degree of comment on Matt's situation as the story unfolded. This, I felt, was in keeping with Korczak's narrative voice in the book which often seems to address the reader directly and invite them to consider what they might've done in Matt's shoes.

It is worth explaining that in the two scenes in the play set in the

2

children's parliament it is intended that the audience assume the role of delegates. They should be encouraged to make proposals, comment and, crucially, vote. The scripted dialogue, particularly in the first of these sections, serves as a kind of safety net. In practice, we discovered that while some audiences were reluctant to do any more than raise their hands to vote, others embraced the debate so enthusiastically that it added ten minutes onto the running time! Though a little nerve-racking for the actors, these sections were often the most exciting and revealing parts of the show.

There are two other elements drawn from Korczak which are also worth mentioning. The first is the opening warning that this is a story for children and so some adults may find it upsetting. This echoes directly Korczak's own introduction to the book. The second is the unresolved nature of the ending. *King Matt the First* ends on what would now be regarded as something of a cliff-hanger. As a consequence, the play ends in similar fashion and, though perhaps a little more abrupt than the book, aims for the same effect of leaving the final unravelling to the imagination of the audience.

Now of course, with this publication of the script, that unravelling will hopefully continue with other readers and other audiences. The play, like its hero, will have to fend for itself in a harsh world. I can only hope it proves as resilient as Matt himself. It'd be nice to think this isn't the end . . . just another cliff-hanger!

'I'll tell you what happened . . . just as soon as I find out!'

(closing line of *King Matt the First*)

Stephen Greenhorn, 2003

Characters

NARRATORS

KING

MINISTERS

DOCTOR

MATT

TUTOR

FOOTMEN

FELEK

GUARD

SOLDIERS

OFFICER

ENEMY GENERAL

ENEMY SOLDIER

GENERALS

OLD KING

PRINCE

POOR KING

BORED KING

JOURNALIST

DELEGATES

TRAIN GUARD

Introduction

NARRATORS: This is a story from not long ago
    And a country not too far from here
    About the things that a boy must learn to let go
    And the things that he ought to hold dear.

    But before the beginning, a warning to all
    Of you grown-up women and men
    That this is a story for those who recall
    What is to be just nine or ten.

    Some of the chapters are gruesome and grim,
    Some of the characters wild,
    And your chances of liking it are pretty darn slim
    'Cause it's meant to be told to a child.

    But sometimes you can't give a grown-up advice;
    There's no way you can make them obey.
    You can warn them the story is not very nice,
    But they won't hear a word that you say.

    So, if you children agree, the grown-ups can stay;
    If you watch them, we'll give them a chance.
    Just make sure your mum isn't sick in her bag
    And your dad doesn't pee in his pants.

    And so there was a king . . .

    And so there was a boy . . .

    And so this is what happened . . .

The King dies

The KING is on his deathbed. The MINISTERS enter.

MINISTERS: The king is sick.
  The king is dying.
  What are we going to do?

Beat.

  If the king dies his son inherits the throne.
  Matt?!
  But he's eleven years old!

Beat.

  He can't write properly.
  He doesn't know geography.
  How can he run the economy if he can't do long division?

Beat.

  It'll be chaos.
  Disaster.
  What're we going to do?

They think. They give up.

MINISTERS: Let's have a drink.

They raise a toast.

MINISTERS: To our great defender . . .
  Our noble monarch . . .
  Our wise leader . . .

The DOCTOR enters. They look at him. He is downcast.

DOCTOR: He is dead.

They MINISTERS still have their glasses raised. They look at each other.

MINISTERS: That means . . .
   The boy becomes . . .
   King Matt!

They are horrified at the idea. They drink to steady their nerves.

Matt's lessons

MATT is surrounded by schoolbooks. His TUTOR enters. MATT is daydreaming.

TUTOR: Now, your majesty if we can return to page three hundred and seventy-two. The past imperfect tense in French is—

MATT interrupts.

MATT: Do you think there's any way someone could become invisible?

The TUTOR is bemused.

TUTOR: If we could return to French grammar. The past imperfect tense—

MATT: Like a magic cloak or something? Or a ring?

A beat.

TUTOR: If we start with the irregular verbs, I think you'll find that—

MATT: 'Cause if there was, I could walk round town without anyone noticing me. As if I wasn't there.

The TUTOR loses patience.

TUTOR: Your Majesty, a king cannot be invisible. A king must be seen. He must be seen by his Ministers. He must be seen by his people. He must be seen by ambassadors from other countries. Like France!

MATT notes the reprimand and goes back to his book. The TUTOR is annoyed at himself for losing his temper. He closes his own book and looks at his watch.

TUTOR: It is seventeen and a half minutes past twelve. Time for your Majesty's walk in the park.

MATT closes his book. A FOOTMAN calls out.

FOOTMAN: Time for his Majesty's walk in the park!

Another FOOTMAN repeats this. And another. And another. And another . . . MATT sighs.

Matt meets Felek

Various FOOTMEN prepare MATT for his walk.

NARRATORS: A young king needs his exercise
    And Matt was no exception.
    But the footmen and the palace guards
    Were charged with his protection.
    So every day at twelve-eighteen
    He'd take his daily bout
    And every day at twelve-o-six
    They'd clear the people out.
    But they never thought to look in the trees . . .

MATT is walking in circles when FELEK drops out of a tree and lands at his feet. MATT is surprised but delighted to meet someone else. FELEK has a handful of apples.

MATT: Are you alright?

FELEK: I'll live.

MATT: What were you doing up there?

FELEK: What does it look like?

MATT: But this is a royal park. You're not supposed to steal the apples.

FELEK squares up to MATT.

FELEK: You going to tell on me?

MATT thinks, then shakes his head. FELEK grins and offers him an apple. MATT takes it. They munch together.

MATT: I think I've seen you before. Playing by the palace wall.

FELEK: That's right. My dad's a lieutenant in the Guard. What does your dad do?

MATT: My father's dead.

Beat.

FELEK: What did he do before?

MATT: He was the king.

FELEK looks at him for a moment, then bursts out laughing and punches MATT on the shoulder.

FELEK: That's a good one! The King! Ha!

MATT: He was! Now it's me.

FELEK laughs again.

FELEK: You're a laugh. King? Wish I was King.

MATT: Why?

FELEK: Why?! So I could do anything I wanted!

MATT thinks about this. FELEK spots a GUARD coming towards them. He prepares to flee.

GUARD: Hey you! Halt!

FELEK: Look out. We've been spotted. You go that way, I'll go this way. Quick.

FELEK heads off.

MATT: What's your name?

FELEK: Felek. Now scarper!

FELEK exits. The GUARD enters, flustered. He suddenly recognises MATT.

GUARD: Your Majesty. That boy . . . What was he up to?

MATT: Boy? . . . What boy?

The GUARD looks at him. MATT doesn't flinch.

Matt and the Ministers

MATT is on the throne. Bored. The MINISTERS are there, presenting him with reports.

MINISTERS: Your Majesty, this is the Foreign Minister's report on our current alliances and border disputes.

And this is from the Minister of War detailing the number of cannons out of commission and soldiers unfit for duty. From the Minister of Finance, Majesty. Explaining the lack of any further financial provision for the Armed Forces.

MATT is bamboozled.

MINISTERS: And the Minister of Education details here some of the problems we're having with the children.

MATT perks up.

MATT: Children? What kind of problems?

MINISTERS: Not studying.

Turning up late.

The boys are sneaking out of classes.

The girls are calling each other names.

Fighting.

Throwing stones.

Breaking windows.

MATT is smiling.

MINISTERS: It's a very serious situation, your Majesty. Very serious.

MATT stops smiling.

MATT: Alright. Is that all?

MINISTERS: Just one more thing, sire.

Following the unfortunate incident the other day in the park . . .

Most unfortunate.

. . . The cabinet have decided that, in future, your Majesty's walks should be confined to the palace gardens.

MATT: But . . .

MINISTERS: It's for your own good, Majesty.

MATT sighs and nods. The MINISTERS bow and exit. MATT tosses the armful of reports onto the floor in annoyance.

Matt whistles

MATT is in the palace gardens walking huffily in small circles when he hears a noise from over the wall. It is FELEK playing. MATT is excited.

MATT: Felek? Is that you?

FELEK: Who's that?

MATT: It's me. We met in the park, remember?

FELEK scrambles over the wall suspiciously.

FELEK: What're you doing in the palace gardens?

MATT: They won't let me out any more.

FELEK: Who?

MATT: The ministers.

The penny drops for FELEK.

FELEK: So you . . . You really are . . . you're the King!

FELEK stands to attention. MATT is surprised. He grabs FELEK and pulls him out of view of the palace.

MATT: Stop that. They'll see you. Then we'll both be in trouble.

FELEK: Excuse me, your Majesty. But you're the King, why do we have to hide?

MATT sighs.

MATT: It's the Ministers. They never let me do anything exciting. All I do is sign papers and sit in lessons. It's all so boring.

FELEK: But it's bound to get more exciting now there's going to be a war.

MATT: What?

FELEK: You don't know?

MATT: They don't tell me anything.

FELEK: Three other kings have declared war on you. I heard from my dad.

MATT: Three?

FELEK: They think you're too young to be a proper king. They want to take over the country and divide it and run it themselves.

MATT is angry.

MATT: They can't do that!

FELEK shrugs. MATT is thinking now.

MATT: Thanks, Felek. At least now I have one person I can trust.

FELEK: At your service, your Highness.

MATT: How can I find you if I need to talk to you again?

FELEK: Just whistle.

FELEK demonstrates, salutes with a grin, then exits. MATT is anxious.

MATT: Too young to be a proper king? We'll see about that!

He exits back to the palace.

War is declared

The MINISTERS are agitated.

MINISTERS: But how did the little runt find out?
　　And what's the snotty brat going to do?
　　Its against the law to talk about the king that way.
　　King? He's not a real king! He's nothing but a jumped up
　　little schoolboy parading around in his father's . . .

MATT enters. The MINISTERS are suddenly polite again.

MINISTERS: Your Majesty!

MATT is serious. The MINISTERS shuffle uneasily.

MATT: So there's going to be a war then?

MINISTERS: It seems that way, your Highness.

MATT: And none of you thought this important enough to
　　mention to your King?

MINISTERS: Well we . . .
　　That is to say . . .
　　You see, the thing was . . .

MATT: Enough! You should be ashamed. The country's about to
　　go to war and you don't tell the King? What kind of Ministers

are you? You're a disgrace!

The MINISTERS look at each other. They take the huff.

MINISTERS: Well, if your Majesty really feels that way . . .
   Our positions would be untenable . . .
   We would have no option . . .
   But to resign . . .
   Forthwith.

MATT is suddenly fazed. He wasn't expecting this and backtracks slightly.

MATT: What? No. I mean. Yes. Yes. That's all very well, but this is war now. You can't suddenly walk out just when I need you.

The MINISTERS realise they have got him.

MINISTERS: Well if your Majesty *needs* us . . .

MATT knows he has lost the battle of wills.

MATT: Uhm. Yes. I've decided, there'll be no resigning till this is all over. I forbid it. Absolutely.

The MINISTERS look at each other, pleased.

MINISTERS: And now sire?

MATT: Now? Now, we must defend the country!

The MINISTERS applaud indulgently, then begin frantically planning and discussing. They do not involve MATT at all. He is marginalised as they exit in an animated little huddle. MATT kicks a chair in frustration at his failure to assert himself.

Matt runs off to war

NARRATORS: And so a war had broken out,
  And Matt had pledged to fight.
  The Cabinet had palmed him off,
  But he had put them right.

  The trouble was he couldn't see
  How the enemy could be fought
  While he was spending all his time
  Taking walks and being taught.

  So patronised, ignored, rebuffed,
  He gave in to frustration;
  He left his schoolbooks far behind
  And went off to save the nation.

  But not on his own . . .

MATT is lurking by the wall. He whistles and FELEK appears.

FELEK: Your Highness.

MATT: Right, Felek. I'm ready. When do we leave?

FELEK: We can sneak on a train tonight, your Highness.

MATT: Felek?

FELEK: Yes, your Highness.

MATT: You'd better stop calling me 'your Highness'.

FELEK: Yes, your Highness.

They laugh.

MATT: You'd better not call me Matt either. Call me . . . Tomek.

FELEK: Okay. Tomek. Let's go.

They sneak off.

Getting on the train

MATT and FELEK sneak along the station platform. It is cloaked in steam and bustling with soldiers who brush past them ignoring them. MATT is sticking close to FELEK for fear of getting lost. FELEK suddenly stops and MATT bumps into him. FELEK pushes him. He is looking around. He nudges MATT to come and join a group of SOLDIERS waiting to board. They try to look inconspicuous, but fail.

SOLDIER: Hey! How old are you?

MATT: Nineteen!

They laugh. Not believing him.

SOLDIER: And where d'you think you're off to?

FELEK: We're going to the war. With you.

The SOLDIERS laugh again.

SOLDIERS: You'll never get on the train
You can get on if you want, but the lieutenant will throw
you back off if he catches you.
When he catches you.

MATT: If he throws us off we'll just walk to the front line!

The SOLDIERS laugh again.

SOLDIERS: That's a long way for your little legs!
  By the time you get there, you might be old enough to
  fight!

FELEK: We're old enough to fight right now.

MATT: Yes. For King and Country!

SOLDIERS: Ho! He's a patriot!
  We're fighting *against* kings, not *for* them.

MATT is puzzled by this remark. The SOLDIERS are interrupted by the train whistle. They spring into action to get on board.

SOLDIERS: Hop to it! Everyone on board!
  Don't hang about!

The SOLDIERS board the train. MATT and FELEK smuggle themselves along with them.

The train to the front

MATT and FELEK are bundled in a freight car with the SOLDIERS.

NARRATORS: Thirty trucks designed for cattle,
  Filled with men and two small boys.
  Thirty trucks of sweat and swearing
  Filled with bumps and smell and noise.

  Thirty hours of shake and rattle,
  Darkness, draughts and cold hard floor.
  Thirty hours to start to realise
  Things are different in a war.

The SOLDIERS kick MATT and FELEK and hand them a bowl. MATT tastes the soup. It is disgusting.

SOLDIERS: Better eat it short-legs. It's all you're going to get.

MATT forces some down.

MATT: I feel sick.

SOLDIERS: Don't even think about it!

MATT and FELEK are thoroughly miserable now.

NARRATORS: Onward 'cross the land and onward,
    Through the night and through the day,
    Front line creeping ever closer,
    Home sweet home further away.

    Half time sleeping, half time waking,
    Most time feeling in a dream,
    Passing time to wheels all clacking,
    Carried on in spits of steam.

The SOLDIERS continue their quarrel.

SOLDIERS: If you ask me, all kings are the same.
    Maybe King Matt is different?
    Yeah? Well where is he?
    Kings have to plan things. Tactics and strategy. That's what they do.
    But you tell me how many kings get killed in a war and how many soldiers like us!

MATT is about to argue but FELEK kicks him.

NARRATORS: Thirty trucks designed for cattle,
    Filled with men and two small boys.
    Thirty trucks of sweat and swearing,
    Filled with bumps and smell and noise.

    Thirty hours of shake and rattle,
    Darkness, draughts and cold hard floor.
    Thirty hours to start to realise
    Things are different in a war.

The train is slowing.

NARRATORS: Things are different in a war.
    Things are different
    In a
    War.

The train stops.

The front line

The sound of distant artillery. The SOLDIERS and FELEK and MATT struggle to their feet. An OFFICER appears.

OFFICER: Fall in!

They fall in. The OFFICER inspects them. He stops at FELEK and MATT.

OFFICER: What kind of soldiers are you meant to be?

MATT: We're just the same as you.

FELEK: Only smaller.

The SOLDIERS laugh.

OFFICER: Silence!

The OFFICER considers the two boys, then passes them each a rifle.

OFFICER: Here. I suppose if you're big enough to carry those, you're big enough to fight.

MATT and FELEK are delighted. The OFFICER receives an order by radio.

OFFICER: Prepare to advance.

The SOLDIERS and MATT and FELEK prepare.

OFFICER: By the left. Quick march.

They march. And march. And march.

OFFICER: Halt!

The OFFICER receives another order.

OFFICER: Prepare to withdraw!

The SOLDIERS groan.

OFFICER: About face. By the left. Quick march.

They march again – in the opposite direction. They are tired now.

OFFICER: Halt. Dig in.

A bigger groan this time. The SOLDIERS start to dig trenches. MATT and FELEK are exhausted. They dig slowly.

MATT: I'm exhausted, Felek. I thought we were coming to fight. Not march back and forth all day then dig trenches.

FELEK: We're soldiers. We've got to follow orders.

The OFFICER sees MATT and FELEK talking. He yells at them.

OFFICER: You two, what do you think this is? A coffee-morning? Stop yapping and dig!

MATT and FELEK dig. The OFFICER moves on. MATT whispers to FELEK.

MATT: I don't see what's so urgent about digging a hole.

A shell suddenly whistles overhead. FELEK jumps on MATT and pulls him into the trench. The shell explodes nearby showering them with dirt. FELEK and MATT sit up and look at one another.

SOLDIERS: Now, d'you see why we dig?
  If it's forward, it's forward.
  If it's back, it's back.
  And if it's dig . . .
  We dig!

FELEK and MATT dig with new enthusiasm.

Trench war

Night. The trenches are lit up with flares and flashes of gunfire. Sound of artillery.

NARRATORS: And so Matt's war just stuttered on
    In fits and starts and bursts of shell;
    A week of doing next to nothing,
    Then a day or two of hell.

    Half the time spent feeling bored,
    And half the time scared half to death;
    Sometimes telling jokes with comrades,
    Sometimes sharing their last breath.

    Two steps forward, one step back;
    No-one gains or loses much,
    Except the poor souls in the trenches,
    Losing weeks and months and touch.

    Matt read books and learned from others,
    Keen to find out everything;
    If he filled his head with knowledge,
    He might forget he was still King . . .

Matt the veteran

Night. MATT and FELEK are battle-hardened now. MATT has a bloody bandage round his head. He chews and spits as he cleans his rifle. The OFFICER creeps along the trench to them with a torch.

FELEK: Lieutentant. What's the word? Are they ordering the advance yet?

OFFICER: Not yet. The Minister of Defence can't decide if it's the right time or not.

MATT: He's a fool. If we don't push now we'll be stuck here all winter.

OFFICER: Let's hope he realises that. In the meantime, I've got a job for one of you. It's dangerous though. I won't order you. I'm asking for a volunteer. What d'you say?

MATT and FELEK exchange a glance then speak together.

MATT and FELEK: I'll do it!

The OFFICER smiles.

OFFICER: Tomek. Your turn, I think. I want you to slip through the wire and go over the enemy line.

MATT nods.

OFFICER: Our artillery need to know where their ammunition dump is. Find it then signal with this so our boys can shell it.

The OFFICER hands him the torch. MATT spits and nods again.

OFFICER: Are you sure you want to do this?

MATT thinks.

MATT: Yeah. I could do with a walk.

The OFFICER pats him on the shoulder and leaves. MATT and FELEK look at each other. FELEK grins.

FELEK: If you're not back by daybreak I'm coming looking for you.

MATT: I'll be back in time for breakfast.

They shake hands. MATT sets out.

Matt the spy

MATT is behind enemy lines. He is moving stealthily, peering at the enemy positions. Suddenly enemy soldiers appear. MATT hides. The soldiers pass. MATT moves on. He stops and peers through binoculars. He spies the ammunition dump. Getting out the torch and a map he begins to signal to his own side the position of the dump. He waits. A shell flies over. There is a small explosion. It missed. Another miss. Then another. The fourth shell finds its target, however, and there is a huge explosion as the dump goes up. MATT dances for joy in the flashing light. He stops suddenly when he realises he has been spotted by an enemy SOLDIER. The SOLDIER has a rifle pointed at him. MATT raises his arms in surrender.

Matt on trial

MATT is under guard before a GENERAL. The SOLDIER who captured him is there too.

GENERAL: Young man, you are accused of spying. If found guilty you will be hanged. Do you understand?

MATT: I'm not a spy.

SOLDIER: He was signalling to the enemy where our ammunition was. I saw him do it. He was celebrating when it was hit.

GENERAL: Is this true? Were you sending signals?

MATT: Yes.

GENERAL: Then you are guilty.

MATT: I'm not a spy.

GENERAL: You've just admitted you directed artillery onto our ammunition dump!

MATT: I wasn't spying. I was on reconnaissance. I'm a soldier.

GENERAL: You're not old enough to be a soldier.

MATT: You think I'm old enough to be a spy!

GENERAL: Less insolence, boy. What use could a soldier your age possibly be?

MATT: I could sneak through your lines, crawl past your sentries, find your ammunition, signal our artillery and blow the whole lot to kingdom come.

The GENERAL is not amused.

GENERAL: Very well, my lad. If that's how you want it. If you were a spy we'd hang you. But if you say you're a soldier, well, we can't do that.

MATT is relieved. The GENERAL speaks to the SOLDIER.

GENERAL: Sentence is death by firing squad.

MATT is shocked. The GENERAL smiles. He stands up and puts a hand on MATT's shoulder.

GENERAL: You see my boy. This is how war is. Not for children.

MATT: I'm not a child. I'm a soldier. And I'll die like one.

GENERAL: You certainly will. Tommorrow at daybreak.

The GENERAL gives MATT an ironic salute then leaves. The SOLDIER stays as guard. MATT sits down, not so bold now, and contemplates his fate.

Matt is rescued

Night. MATT is pacing in the moonlight.

NARRATORS: Imagine the thoughts of a prisoner-of-war
   'Neath the bright moon that gleams like a knife,
   Preparing himself for a dawn that brings death
   When he's only just started with life.

   Does he dwell on regrets? On what might've been?
   Does he curse his mistakes through the night?
   Or does he choose to remember the lessons he's learned
   And feel proud of the things he got right?

   Or does he wonder if anyone knows where he is?
   What surprises the new day might bring?
   'Cause remember the rarest of deaths in a war
   Is the death of an unrescued king!

MATT hears this last remark and puzzles over it as the faint sound of aeroplanes is heard overhead. He listens and begins to wonder. The aeroplane drone gets louder. Then MATT hears a familiar whistle. He can't believe it.

MATT: Felek!

The sound of bombs falling. MATT ducks. A bomb whistles to the ground nearby and there is huge explosion. Blackout.

MATT is revealed.

MATT recovers consciousness in a hospital bed. He is bandaged. By the bed are some of his own GENERALS. MATT notices them. The GENERALS salute him.

GENERALS: Your Majesty is feeling a little better, I trust.

> The doctors expect your Majesty to have a slight headache for a few days . . .
>
> . . . but nothing more serious.
>
> Thank the Lord.

MATT leaps out of bed and salutes them.

MATT: Sir. Private Tomek. Reporting for duty. Sir.

The GENERALS chuckle a little.

GENERALS: Felek!

> Can you come in here a moment?

FELEK enters. He sees MATT and grins at him before saluting.

FELEK: Forgive me, your Majesty. I had to tell them.

MATT realises his cover has been blown.

GENERALS: In the capital they thought you were dead, sire.

> There were riots.
>
> Talk of revolution.
>
> The army was close to deserting.

FELEK: When we heard you'd been captured I had to tell them who you really were.

The GENERALS beckon MATT over to a campaign table where a map of the front is spread out. It is covered with little markers. The GENERALS point out where MATT was held.

GENERAL: We mounted a rescue mission.

    Artillery.

    And bombing.

    A diversion. Meanwhile . . .

FELEK: I came and found you!

MATT: So it was you!

FELEK: And the Lieutenant.

MATT: Where is he? I ought to thank him.

A beat.

FELEK: He didn't make it.

MATT takes this in.

MATT: I'm sorry. He was a good man. He taught me a lot.

MATT gazes at the campaign map. He is thinking.

MATT: Are our stocks of fuel and ammunition high?

GENERALS: Yes, your Highness.

MATT: Have the men in the front line been given the new issue of boots?

GENERALS: Yes your Highness.

MATT: And has this week's bread ration been distributed?

GENERALS: Yes your Highness.

MATT: Then the army is ready.

GENERALS: For what, your Highness?

MATT stabs at the campaign table.

MATT: Tomorrow we launch the general attack.

The GENERALS look at one another.

GENERALS: Your Highness, the Minister for Defence . . .
He hasn't reached a decision, yet.

MATT: The men have spent six months in stinking trenches
waiting for the Minister to decide. I don't intend to leave
them there a day longer.

A beat.

MATT: I am not Private Tomek any more. I am King Matt. And I
say we attack now while we have the chance.

The GENERALS are delighted.

GENERALS: Of course, your Majesty.
Excellent, sir.
We cannot fail.

MATT: We must not fail, gentlemen.

**The GENERALS salute and exit. FELEK is excited. MATT is
studying the campaign table.**

FELEK: You're a real live hero now, you know.

MATT: A hero?

FELEK: When the troops heard that the King had been serving
alongside them on the front line all this time, and carrying
out dangerous missions, they wanted to make you a saint!

MATT smiles.

FELEK: Just think. Now you can ride along the lines on
horseback like a real king and all the men'll cheer you.
Imagine. You in your uniform on a great white horse!

MATT: Do you think a white horse is a good idea for leading an attack?

FELEK: Not for the attack, for the victory parade!

MATT starts to get caught up in FELEK's excitement.

MATT: Yes. We'll fight and win and drive the enemy away and go home to the city.

FELEK: And you can ride your white horse through the streets. With all the people cheering.

MATT: Throwing their hats in the air!

MATT jumps on FELEK's back and they canter round the room laughing.

FELEK: Shouting for the King. Chanting your name. Can you imagine it! King Matt! King Matt! King Matt!

They canter off, still chanting.

Matt the reformer

NARRATORS: The army had been waiting for
This one decisive order;
With Matt in charge they pushed the foe
Right back across the border.

With all invaders driven out,
Matt declared the war would end there.
He accepted unconditionally
His enemies' surrender.

On a white horse with a cheering crowd
Matt paraded in the sun.
But what's a warrior king to do
When the war he's won is done?

Faint sound of a crowd chanting Matt's name. The cheering and shouting grows louder. The MINISTERS are nervously awaiting the arrival of the King. MATT enters wearing an army greatcoat and a row of medals. The MINISTERS bow.

MINISTERS: Majesty.
Your Highness.
So good to have you back, sire.

MATT: Hah! Don't start all that. I know what you've been up to. Mucking things up here while I've been out fighting a damned war. Well, I'm back now, d'you hear? And you bunch of sickwits better watch out. Or else.

The MINISTERS are shocked at his rough speech.

MINISTERS: Sire. The army seems to have undone some of your regal bearing.

MATT: Tough. I'm still the King. If any of you don't like it, there's a platoon of soldiers in the corridor ready to show you the inside of a cell.

The MINISTERS get defensive.

MINISTERS: Beg your pardon, sire, but according to Volume 814 of the Laws and Regulations, Section 71 Paragraph 12 . . . The Monarch may not, without the—

MATT: I don't care what the law says.

MINISTERS: If your Majesty violates the law, then I'm afraid Section 202, Paragraphs 18 and 61 come in to play—

MATT: Stop it. You're bugging me.

MINISTERS: Ah! Covert surveillance and listening devices are
dealt with in Subsection 44 of Appendix 29.

MATT: Enough!

MINISTERS: It's the law, sire. That's what your Ministers are here
for. To help you understand the law.

MATT considers.

MATT: And what if I just say, blast the law, and have you all
thrown in jail?

MINISTERS: I'm afraid you would be officially regarded as a
Tyrant.
Like your great uncle, Henrik the Horrible.
You would be . . . Matt the Merciless.
One wouldn't wish for that, would one, Majesty.

MATT: I suppose not.

MINISTERS: One really needs to know the law, sire.

MATT: And how long before one knows it well enough to do
without one's Ministers?

The MINISTERS confer.

MINISTERS: Oooh. Maybe thirty . . . ?
Perhaps nearer forty . . . ?
I would say fifty.
Yes. Fifty.
Fifty years.
At least.

MATT: Fifty years!! Damn and shrapnel! That's forever!

MINISTERS: Indeed, Majesty. Which is why we remain at your
disposal.

The MINISTERS are smug now.

MATT: You're telling me I can't run the country myself.

MINISTERS: There are many things you, as yet, know little of,
    I'm afraid, sire.
    Complex things.
    Grown-up things.

MATT: I see. I'm young so I can't rule grown-ups properly. But
    you're old and you think you're perfectly qualified to rule the
    children?

The MINISTERS laugh nervously.

MINISTERS: But sire, we have experience.
    We were young once ourselves.

MATT: Once. Not any more. You're old now.

MINISTER: Not *that* old, sire.

MATT: You. What age are you?

MINISTERS: Me? Why, I'm only . . . fifty-seven.

**MATT laughs. The MINISTER is embarrassed. MATT is
thinking fast. He has an idea.**

MATT: Right. Here's what we'll do then . . .

The MINISTERS are startled again.

MATT: You're right, I don't know about boring grown-up laws, so
    maybe I do need your help with those. But I'm perfectly
    capable of running the things I do know about.

MINISTERS: Which are . . . ?
    Majesty?

MATT: Children. I can rule the children without your interference.

The MINISTERS are bemused.

MATT: If I know anything, I know what young people need.

MINISTERS: But sire . . .

MATT: I have decided.

MINISTER: I'm afraid it is impossible.

MATT glares at him.

MATT: Impossible?

MINISTER: You see, according to the law, children are the property of their parents.

MATT fixes them with an icy stare.

MATT: Then I'll damn well change that law!

The MINISTERS look at each other.

MINISTERS: Yes, I suppose . . .
　A few changes could be passed. . .
　If you do it this way, you'd not be breaking the law, you'd
　be improving it.
　You would be a Reformer!

MATT: King Matt the Reformer!
　I like that.

MINISTERS: It has a ring to it.
　A certain class.
　Very fitting.

MATT: Alright then, for my next reform . . .

He thinks, then has an idea.

MATT: Each schoolchild to be given a pound of chocolate tomorrow!

The MINISTERS look at one another. MATT sees.

MATT: Something wrong with my reform?

MINISTER: A pound is too much, sire. They'll all be sick.

MATT: A quarter-pound then. Tomorrow morning.

MINISTER: There are a million schoolchildren in the country, sire. It'll take at least a week to produce so much chocolate.

MATT: Very well. In seven days.

MINISTER: I'm afraid transport hasn't recovered from the war yet, sire. Distribution will take at least a fortnight.

MATT: All right. Fine. A quarter pound of chocolate for every child in three weeks' time.

The MINISTERS nod. This is possible.

MATT: But let's at least announce the reform tomorrow.

MINISTERS: Thing is sire, we can't really call it a reform. We're not changing any laws. It's more a sort of . . . treat.

MATT: All right. All right. Just call it a treat then.

MINISTERS: Very good Majesty.
A quarter pound of chocolate for every child in three weeks' time as a special treat.
It'll make a fine headline.

MATT is worn down with this negotiation.

MATT: This is worse than digging trenches. You're making my

head hurt. I'm going for a walk.

MATT exits. The MINISTERS sigh with relief.

MINISTERS: Matt the Reformer? Whatever next!
Ridiculous idea, him ruling the children.
It'll never work.
Let him have the brats. Keeps them out of our hair.
We've bigger things to worry about.
Like where are we going to borrow the money to pay for everything?

They groan collectively as they remember this problem. They exit.

Matt and Felek

MATT is in the garden thinking. He hears a whistle. FELEK enters, grinning. He salutes him. MATT hugs him.

MATT: Felek! You're back home. I haven't seen you since the victory parade.

FELEK nods.

FELEK: They gave me a medal.

MATT: You're a war hero. What did your dad say to that?

FELEK scowls.

FELEK: He just gave me a hiding for running away in the first place.

FELEK sits down beside MATT.

MATT: Don't worry. I'm going to put a stop to that kind of thing.

FELEK: Do you think you can do it by tomorrow? He doesn't know I lost his penknife yet.

MATT: Sorry, Felek. Reforming seems to be a slow process.

FELEK: But you're the King.

MATT: Even Kings can't do everything they want. Not all at once.

FELEK: That's no fun.

MATT: I have to make sure I do things properly.

FELEK: 'Properly.' Sounds like in the army!

MATT: There are rules everywhere.

FELEK: Rules are made to be broken, I say!

He gets up.

FELEK: Does King Matt feel like 'reforming' the number of apples in the royal park?

MATT looks at him. He grins. They exit laughing.

A diplomatic mission

NARRATORS: So the children got their chocolate,
   And Matt became their hero,
   But the balance at the treasury
   Was getting close to zero.

   The Ministers hatched a desperate plan
   Which they put to Matt in writing.
   They wanted him to borrow from
   The Kings they'd just been fighting!

MATT: But I don't understand, how can we be broke?

MINISTERS: Wars cost money, sire.
Especially when one wins.
And the peace terms you offered them were . . . ahem . . .
generous.

MATT: But there weren't any terms.

MINISTERS: Exactly!

MATT is a little regretful at his mistake.

NARRATORS: And so a Royal Tour was planned:
Matt knew he had to go,
Be charming and noble to all of his hosts
Then ask them for some dough!

The station. Crowds are cheering. Flags. Steam. The MINISTERS are seeing MATT off.

MINISTERS: Please be very careful sire.
Try not to sign anything.
They'll try to trick you.

MATT: I managed to outwit them on the battlefield, didn't I.

MINISTERS: Yes, Majesty, but this is politics. It's more dangerous than war.

A beat.

MINISTERS: They'll be pretending to be your friends, but they'll just be trying to get things their own way.

MATT looks at them.

MATT: I've met people like that before.

The MINISTERS are a little embarrassed. MATT boards the

train. He waves to the crowd.

MINISTERS: Don't forget sire. We're depending on you.
    We have every confidence!

MATT nods and waves. The train pulls away.

MINISTERS: What d'you think?
    No chance.

NARRATORS: The Royal Train is very posh,
    But the wheels still shake and rattle;
    Matt travelled on the very line
    Which carried him to battle.

    But this time things were different:
    A deal had to be done.
    And Matt had to be the perfect guest
    With the Old King number one.

The Old King

**The OLD KING is accompanied by his brooding son, the
PRINCE. They await MATT's arrival at the station.**

PRINCE: I hear he's calling himself the Reformer now. He's
    coming to cause trouble.

OLD KING: Not this time my boy. He needs our help. He'll be
    friendly as can be. And so will we.

PRINCE: Why?

OLD KING: Because we're not ready for another war.

PRINCE: Not yet.

The train stops. Music and cheering. MATT steps off and is greeted by the OLD KING with much kissing of cheeks.

OLD KING: My son and I bid you welcome, my young friend. Welcome to my Kingdom. Know that you come here not just as a conqueror of armies, but as a conqueror of people's hearts.

MATT smiles politely. The PRINCE forces himself to say his own piece.

PRINCE: We welcome the good and valiant King Matt. May your reign be long and fruitful.

MATT smiles, touched by this reception. The OLD KING nudges him towards a microphone.

OLD KING: Please. Say a few words. The people want to hear from you.

MATT nervously approaches the microphone.

MATT: I am your friend!

Huge cheers. Cannons fire. MATT waves to the crowd.

OLD KING: See how they cheer you!

PRINCE: They cheer because there are cannons pointed at them.

OLD KING: He is too young to suspect such a trick.

PRINCE: Look at him. A boy sent to do a man's job!

OLD KING: Yes. But we must give him what he wants.

PRINCE: For now, father. Just for now.

The PRINCE and the OLD KING smile woodenly and wave to the crowds too.

NARRATORS: There were crowds and cheers and gala balls,
　　And trips out to the funfair;
　　And though Matt welcomed all of these,
　　He remembered why he'd gone there.

　　A handshake sealed the money loan,
　　There was a leaving do,
　　Then it was back on the train again,
　　To meet Poor King number two.

The OLD KING and the PRINCE exit.

The Poor King

MATT is joined by the POOR KING.

POOR KING: So how do you like my capital, young King Matt?

MATT: It's very beautiful.

POOR KING: I'm glad you think so. We are a small kingdom. Poor in resources. We have no great buildings like our neighbours, but what we have we make the most of.

MATT: You have things here I've never seen before.

POOR KING: Really? Such as?

MATT: You have a zoo! All those animals! It's amazing.

POOR KING: I have friends in many countries where these animals are living. They send them to me. Maybe they could send some to you also.

MATT: I would like that very much. But I would have to build a zoo first to have somewhere to put them.

POOR KING: So why don't you build a zoo?

MATT: I'd like to, your Majesty. But that kind of project would cost a lot of money. The war has left us poor – even though it was not us who started it.

The POOR KING looks at MATT and realises he is about to get down to business. He laughs and claps his hand on the boy's shoulder.

POOR KING: King Matt. You know how to tug at a nation's heart. Let us talk money, then. Maybe I can help you.

MATT smiles. They begin to negotiate.

NARRATORS: A couple of lions, a tiger or two,
　　An elephant and a giraffe,
　　A gorilla for eating bananas,
　　And a hyena just for a laugh.

　　The Poor King agreed to the loan deal,
　　Though he charged an exorbitant fee;
　　So Matty soon said his goodbyes to the zoo,
　　And went off to meet King number three.

The Bored King

The BORED KING has prepared a concert for MATT. A fast and furious jig is played. It finishes and MATT applauds eagerly. He notices the BORED KING is clapping only politely.

MATT: That was fun.

BORED KING: If you like that sort of thing, I suppose.

MATT: You don't like it?

BORED KING: Not much.

MATT: Then why don't you play music you like?

BORED KING: Because I'm the King. It's not about what I like. It's about the people. What they want. And what they seem to want is music you can dance to.

MATT: Surely there's a way you can keep the people happy and be happy yourself at the same time?

The BORED KING laughs.

BORED KING: Ah Matt, you certainly have a lot to learn. Making people happy can be a difficult business. Let me show you something.

The BORED KING steers MATT to a balcony.

BORED KING: You see that building? I thought that would make my people happy.

MATT: What is it? A cathedral? An opera-house?

BORED KING: It's a Parliament.

MATT: What's a Parliament?

BORED KING: In my country the people elect the ministers. The Parliament is where the ministers go to argue and discuss and make decisions.

MATT: The people choose the ministers?

BORED KING: Yes. And if things are going badly they can get rid of them and elect new ones.

MATT: And can they get rid of the King?

BORED KING: If they wanted to.

MATT: So you're afraid the people will want to get rid of you?

BORED KING: No. I'd be happy to step down. But things are never as simple as that. That's the problem. It's so difficult to decide anything. There are always arguments. I can't tell if they're happier now or not.

MATT: But it must be better now that everyone has a say?

The BORED KING nods.

BORED KING: Better? Yes. Easier? No.

MATT is thinking.

MATT: Grown-ups always seem to make things so complicated. That's why my reforms are going to start with the children.

BORED KING: Reforms?

MATT: I want to build a zoo and make summer camps so that all the poor children in the city can go to the country for a holiday.

BORED KING: That's a good idea.

MATT: But we haven't any money. That's why I'm here. I want to ask you to lend us some.

BORED KING: It's not up to me. The Parliament will have to decide. But I don't think the ministers would be keen to lend such an amount to any one person – not even a King.

MATT thinks.

MATT: Well, what if I had a Parliament? What if my people elected ministers like you do? Then your Parliament could lend to my Parliament.

BORED KING: That'd mean changing your constitution. Do you think you could do that?

MATT: Why not? I'm King Matt the Reformer!

BORED KING: I wish you luck, my boy!

The BORED KING starts to laugh. He puts an arm round MATT's shoulder and leads him off, still laughing. MATT is not offended but a little bemused.

NARRATORS: So young King Matt took the train back home,
    His mission completed in style;
    His Ministers met him, heard the good news,
    And applauded his cunning and guile.

    With three loans secured they could start to rebuild:
    Their reaction was close to ecstatic.
    They even accepted the price they must pay
    That the country must go democratic.

    A Parliament building would have to be built
    Alongside King Matt's proposed zoo;
    They could only hope that things turned out well
    And no one would confuse the two!

Constitutional change

The MINISTERS enter with MATT. The MINISTERS are flustered. MATT is businesslike.

MATT: So, are the railroads finally repaired?

MINISTER: Yes, your Majesty.

MATT: And have the new factories been built?

MINISTER: Yes, your Majesty.

MATT: And the constitution?

MINISTER: The sub-committee have prepared a draft for your perusal.

He hands MATT the draft. MATT looks it over.

MATT: What about plans for the summer camps?

MINISTER: The finance committee suggest spreading the costs over two financial years.

MATT: Fine.

MINISTER: Oh, and the architects expect to have the final designs for the new Parliament ready within a few weeks.

MATT: Good. Anything else?

The MINISTERS have to think for a moment – business has been conducted so swiftly.

MINISTERS: Nothing important.
There's a journalist who wants to see you but he's—

MATT: Send him in.

MINISTERS: He's a journalist, sire.
I really think—

MATT: Send him in and close the door on your way out.

MINISTERS: Yes, your Majesty.

They exit. The JOURNALIST enters. MATT sizes him up.

JOURNALIST: Majesty. Thank you for seeing me.

MATT: What can I do for you?

JOURNALIST: I wanted to talk to you about your reforms.

MATT: What about them?

JOURNALIST: I was wondering exactly how far you were planning to go?

MATT: Well, we're changing the constitution. Giving power to the people.

JOURNALIST: Yes. But then what? Will there be more or will you take a break?

MATT: I'd love a break but not while there's so much work to be done.

JOURNALIST: So you are planning more reforms?

MATT: Does that surprise you?

JOURNALIST: I just wonder if people will need a bit of time to get used to all this first.

MATT: Children adapt quickly.

JOURNALIST: You're planning reforms for children?

MATT: Children must have a role in this new process too.

JOURNALIST: But isn't their role just to do as their parents tell them?

MATT snorts with indignation.

MATT: That's a typical grown-up's attitude! I'm going to change all that.

The JOURNALIST begins to sense a story.

MATT: What I want to do is create a children's parliament alongside the adult one. So the children would be able to elect their own members and have their own say about the things which concern them.

JOURNALIST: A children's parliament?!

The JOURNALIST is surprised, but then begins scheming.

JOURNALIST: What a fantastic idea!

MATT: Do you think so?

JOURNALIST: Of course. But why not give them their own newspaper as well? They could read about what concerns *them* and what's going on in *their* parliament?

MATT: It would mean they were all informed. And I would know about what was going on too.

JOURNALIST: Exactly. And you know if you wanted some help in setting that up, I would happily offer my services as an advisor.

MATT considers this.

MATT: I think you should start right away.

JOURNALIST: Of course, your Majesty.

The JOURNALIST smiles and exits.

Matt the Diplomat

MATT is frantically busy throughout the next narration, gradually becoming more weary.

NARRATORS: Poor Matt, he wanted to be a real King
 And have everyone dance to his tune:
 Perhaps if he'd known how hard it would be,
 He might not've spoken so soon.

 There's architects, bricklayers, carpenters too,
 And plumbers and glaziers as well,
 There's sawmills and factories and brickyards to see,
 And lots of instructions to tell.

There's animals coming in trains from the south,
And steel coming in from the north.
There's an albino elephant that's so flipping rare
No one can say what it's worth.

There's meetings and lessons and letters to write,
There's signing till one's hand is sore,
And as if all of this stuff just wasn't enough
There's talk of a second big war . . .

A MINISTER has entered. MATT is startled.

MATT: War! Did you say *war*?

MINISTER: Yes, your Highness. Some of the other kings are not at all happy with your reforms. They think you're starting to make them look bad.

MATT: Which kings?

MINISTER: The main threat is from the Old King – or rather his son, the Prince. His army is gathering by the border.

MATT: But we can't have a war now. There's too much going on.

MINISTER: I know, your Highnesss. That's the problem. The Prince is worried that his people will revolt when they see what you're doing for the people here.

MATT: We should bring them here. All of them. Then they can see what we're doing. We should invite them to the opening of the parliaments.

MINISTER: Excellent idea, sire. You should write to them tonight.

MATT: Tonight? But I've already been up since . . .

MINISTER: Time is of the essence, I'm afraid.

MATT: You're right. It's important. I'll do it tonight.

The MINISTER nods and exits. MATT gets on with the invites, gradually collapsing with weariness.

NARRATORS: All through the night and on through the dawn,
Poor Matt had to do the right thing,
Till the last one was done and he began to wind down,
Like a clock which has broken its spring.

MATT flops over.

Preparing for Parliament

The JOURNALIST bursts in, clutching a paper. MATT wakens with a start.

JOURNALIST: Your Highness, look! The first edition of the children's paper. It's finally out. It's got all the election results and everything. I'm very impressed with it.

MATT looks at the paper.

JOURNALIST: We've put you on the front, of course. The greatest king in the history of the world!

MATT: Very flattering.

JOURNALIST: And inside, you see, Felek got elected. He's to be the first child prime minister in the world.

MATT: (**reads**) 'Matt has conquered grown-up Kings and Felek will conquer grown-up ministers.'

JOURNALIST: D'you like it?

MATT: (**reads**) 'How can grown-ups be allowed to govern us when they can't even dance properly? They're so ancient

they can't hear the music for the sound of their old bones
rattling.'

JOURNALIST: Wrote that myself.

MATT: It's not very nice to poke fun at people because of their
age.

JOURNALIST: Oh come on, your Highness. Where's your sense
of humour?

MATT: I'm sorry. I'm tired. Maybe that's why I don't see the joke.

JOURNALIST: You should look after yourself, your Highness.
We're depending on you. You still have a lot to do.

MATT: I know. I know.

JOURNALIST: I'll leave you to it, then.

**The JOURNALIST exits. MATT watches him go, thinking
and frowning. He is grumpy and tired. He tears up the
paper and throws it to the ground.**

Parliament opens

NARRATORS: Matt is working far too hard;
    If he got holidays he'd take them,
    But he's made so many promises,
    And he can't afford to break them.

    His reforms are now all coming good,
    Even the most ambitious;
    So why is he getting paranoid
    And feeling so suspicious?

    Here is his children's parliament,
    The first and only one;

Here are Emperors, Kings and Princes,
And a boy who gets things done.

Here's diplomacy and politics
And the world within his reach;
Here's King Matt the Reformer,
To give the opening speech.

MATT enters regally. He addresses the audience as the parliament.

MATT: Friends. Delegates. You have no idea how happy I am to see you here today. Until now I have struggled alone. I have tried to make life better for everyone. But it is very hard for one person to know exactly what is needed to help so many. It will be easier for you, if you work together. You know the cities. You know the country. You know brothers and sisters. You know friends and, now, you know each other. I hope some day that children all over the world will meet like this and discuss what is needed. For now though, I am happy for what we have here. I salute you all. I salute the world's first children's parliament!

Wild cheering. MATT waves and steps to one side. He suddenly looks exhausted. The BORED KING approaches him.

BORED KING: My friend, you are indeed King Matt the Reformer. Congratulations.

MATT: Thank you.

BORED KING: Be warned, though. Reforms do not always go so smoothly. I wish you luck with whatever you are planning next.

MATT nods.

MATT: The only thing I'm planning next is a holiday!

The BORED KING pats his shoulder, then turns away to watch the fireworks.

Parliament in session

MATT suns himself on a deckchair upstage. FELEK takes the chair of the Parliament and addresses the audience. The JOURNALIST skulks around taking notes. FELEK bangs a gavel.

FELEK: I am Prime Minister Felek. I declare this first session of the children's parliament open.

Cheers. The JOURNALIST whispers something in FELEK's ear. FELEK agrees.

FELEK: Let's begin with something easy. Does anyone have anything to say about the summer camps?

Pause.

VOICES: There were holes in the roof.
    And they didn't change the sheets.
    The food was disgusting.
    Not fit for pigs.
    And they beat us if we complained!

Mild uproar. The JOURNALIST notes it all. FELEK bangs his gavel.

FELEK: Order! Order! Comrade delegates! Thank you for your comments, but this is a period of change. Nothing is perfect at first.

Murmurs. The JOURNALIST whispers again. Again FELEK takes the prompt.

FELEK: Okay. Maybe we should be focussing on what we *want* now. That's what this parliament is for. Expressing our wishes.

A beat.

VOICES: I wish I had a rabbit.
    I want a dog.
    And every kid should have a watch!

Some agreement.

VOICES: We don't want aunties kissing us!

Loud yeugh.

VOICES: And no more fried cabbage.
    We should all have bikes.
    I want more pockets in my trousers. I've got too much stuff to put in them.
    Every day should be Christmas.
    Two birthdays a year.
    We should be allowed to break a window once a month.
    No spelling tests!
    Or detention!
    Little kids should be banned!

A cheer.

VOICES: And girls!

Uproar. FELEK bangs his gavel.

FELEK: Shut up! Cut it out! Order comrades or I'll have you all thrown out the door!

Uneasy calm descends.

FELEK: We have to debate and vote. We can't just shout out demands. We need proposals. Now what was first?

JOURNALIST: That every child should have a watch.

VOICES: We need watches 'cause we get punished if we're late for school or dinner or miss a bus.
Why should we have to rely on other people's clocks?
You need a watch to see how long you can hold your breath too!
But if we have a watch we'll have to be on time for everything.

FELEK: All right. So let's put it to the vote. Every child should have a vote. All those in favour?

Hands shoot up.

FELEK: Against?

Fewer hands.

FELEK: The proposal is passed!

Cheers.

FELEK: Next?

The JOURNALIST checks his notes.

JOURNALIST: No kissing from aunties.

FELEK: That's right. Who proposed that?

VOICES: Me. I'm fed up getting slobbered on every time some smelly relative comes to visit.
Me too. It was my birthday last week. There was so much

kissing I thought I was going to throw up.
And it's not just aunts. Parents, uncles, cousins . . .

If grown-ups are so keen on all that stuff let them do it to
each other and leave us alone!
No. That's even worse. My mum and dad kiss all the time.
It's horrible.

FELEK: Right. A vote. No kissing from relatives. Those in favour?

Hands again.

FELEK: Against?

Hands.

FELEK: Carried!

Cheer.

FELEK: Right, now we're flying along. What was next?

The JOURNALIST smiles.

JOURNALIST: Girls should be abolished.

FELEK: Ah, now hold on . . .

VOICES: Girls are crybabies.
    They talk too much.
    They're stuck up too.
    They're boring.
    And scratch you.
    Or tell on you.
    They can't play football.
    Or throw properly.
    Or run!

Laughter.

FELEK: All right. That's enough.

VOICES: Boys are smelly.
They're always fighting.
And break things.
Like windows.
And they shout too much.
And never wash properly.
Boys are lazy.
They never study.
Or do their homework.

Uproar.

VOICES: Go play with your dolls!
You go and have a bath stinky boy!
Who are you telling what to do?
You're to stupid to know!

More uproar. FELEK tries to restore order, but doesn't succeed. He bangs his gavel and starts shouting at people.

VOICES: Away and squeeze your spots!
You can't even spell delegate!

A minor riot ensues. FELEK bangs the gavel again. Shouting.

FELEK: This session's closed. Finished. Get out! Go on, beat it!
Everybody out of here or I'll have you arrested!

The Parliament clears. The JOURNALIST is the last to leave, grinning, as he notes everything down. MATT stretches in his deckchair – oblivious.

Felek visits Matt

FELEK approaches MATT in his deckchair. MATT is delighted to see him, but FELEK looks serious.

MATT: Felek! It's good to see you!

A beat.

MATT: Why are you looking so serious?

FELEK: I'm here on official business.

FELEK produces a document. MATT is disappointed.

MATT: What's this?.

FELEK: I want you to ratify my proposals regarding status and title.

MATT: Pardon?

FELEK: I sent you a letter.

MATT: I thought that was a joke.

FELEK: It is no joking matter, your Majesty. It is important that the Parliament be given proper status.

MATT: What d'you want me to do?

FELEK: First. My name won't be Felek any more, but Baron Felix von Rauch. Second, the children's parliament will now be known as the Progress Parliament – Proparl for short.

MATT: Anything else?

FELEK: Yes, your Highness, I think you should call yourself Emperor Matthew the First.

MATT: I think I'm happy with plain old King Matt, thanks.

FELEK: Very well, your Highness, but I insist that I now be known as Baron von Rauch, Premier of the Proparl.

MATT: Is that really what you want?

FELEK: Yes. Thank you, your Highness.

MATT: Is that all?

FELEK: Also, I think the Premier of the Proparl should have his own office. And limousine. And a salary the same as the grown up Prime Minister.

MATT nods wearily. He signs FELEK's document.

MATT: Very well.

FELEK: Thank you, your Highness.

MATT: Wait. D'you fancy going swimming or something?

FELEK: I'm afraid I must return to the Proparl at once. Official business.

FELEK salutes and exits. MATT sighs. He is worried. He starts to pack. Time to go home.

Things fall apart

NARRATORS: When coming home from holidays
We look with strangers' eyes,
And things once thought familiar
Can take us by surprise.

Sometimes this is refreshing,
Sometimes it will confuse,
Sometimes it's just a matter of
Catching up with all the news.

When Matt returned from his short break
He expected this sensation;
But he didn't think he'd come home to
A crisis in the nation.

MATT is pacing up and down angrily, reading the newspaper. He throws it down in disgust as the MINISTERS file in sheepishly.

MATT: I'm gone for a few weeks and I come back to this! What's happening here? On the way from the station there are demonstrations. People marching and shouting.

MINISTER: That'll be the teachers, Majesty.

MATT: Then by the palace gates there's a whole mob of youths yelling at me.

MINISTER: The sixteen-year-olds, sire. They're complaining that they are too young for the adult parliament but too old for the children's parliament.

MATT: Ah yes. The children's parliament that almost passed a resolution abolishing *girls*!!

MINISTER: It didn't actually pass it, your Highness.

MATT: No, apparently they just had a punch-up instead.

A beat.

MINISTER: It is true to say there is some unrest, your Majesty.

MATT: Unrest? It looks like a riot out there!

MINISTER: It's not that bad, sire. Not yet.

MATT: So what is going on? Why are the teachers out?

MINISTER: It's the children, sire. They're completely out of control. They won't study. Or keep quiet in class. They laugh at authority. They say if they are punished they'll complain to the King. Or pass a resolution.

MATT groans.

MINISTER: The teachers don't know what to do. They've told me they're ready to quit in a week if things aren't resolved. Frankly, a lot of them have already gone. The situation is desperate.

MATT: So it seems.

MINISTER: It's not just the children, your Majesty. The grown-ups are causing problems too. They think they've lost too much power. They say something must be done. Before they take matters into their own hands.

MATT: What does that mean?

MINISTER: There is talk on the streets of revolution, Majesty.

MATT sits down. His head in his hands thinking. He sits up.

MATT: Right. This is what we'll do. Every student will be treated as a worker. They'll be paid a salary to go to school. Paid for the work they do there. Forget the chocolate. We'll give them a salary – but only if they behave and study, otherwise, nothing.

The MINISTERS look at one another.

MINISTERS: It's a brilliant plan, sire . . .
    And it just might work. . .
    But there is one problem. . .

MATT waits.

MINISTERS: The new constitution, sire.
If you want this reform passed you will have to take it to Parliament.
The children's Parliament.

MATT realises that this is indeed the case. He groans. The MINISTERS sneak out.

Matt at the Parliament

The Parliament forms around MATT, who is still sitting with his head in his hands. FELEK is in the chair and the JOURNALIST is still hovering about. FELEK bangs his gavel. MATT looks up.

FELEK: Alright, so you've all heard what the King is proposing. A salary for students. But only if we go to school and behave ourselves.

The DELEGATES mutter. The JOURNALIST whispers in FELEK's ear.

FELEK: I propose we refer the matter to a subcommittee for discussion.

Murmurs of approval.

MATT: But the subcommittee will take too long. The teachers will be gone by the end of the week.

DELEGATES: Good riddance!
But if we don't have teachers we'll never learn anything.
Why don't we keep the teachers but abolish the schools?
Why can't we run the schools and only keep the good teachers?

How can you tell a good teacher from a bad one?
If we can't tell who can?
Certainly not my mum and dad!

Hubbub of agreement.

MATT: Delegates, you don't understand how serious this is. The country's in uproar. You need to make the right decision and make it right now.

The DELEGATES murmur. The JOURNALIST whispers something in FELEK's ear. MATT notices. FELEK turns to MATT.

FELEK: Comrade Majesty.
Can I ask you, have you yourself ever actually *been* to a school?

MATT: No.

FELEK: Have you ever been bullied or beaten up in a playground?

MATT: No.

FELEK: Have you ever been caned or belted or had your ear twisted by a teacher?

MATT: No.

FELEK: Have you ever been given detention or punishment exercises or a nasty note to take home to your parents?

MATT: No.

A beat.

FELEK: You see, it seems to me, sire, that the problem here is that you simply don't understand what it's like at our schools. You don't know how brutal and unfair they can be. You've no idea of the cruelties and humiliations children are subjected to. It seems to me that in this case you're just like most grown-ups. You're very quick to tell us what we should be doing but when it comes down to it you don't actually know what you're talking about. I say, until *everyone* knows what it's like in these places, *no one* should be trying to force us back there.

FELEK addresses the DELEGATES with a grin.

FELEK: Comrades, I propose that the King's suggestion is duly considered by a subcommittee. But in the meantime, in the interests of fairness . . . I propose that it's the grown-ups who are made to go to school!

Cheering. MATT tries to be heard above it to no avail.

FELEK: All those in favour!

Hands up and shouts and yells.

FELEK: The motion is carried!!

Uproar. MATT is distraught. The JOURNALIST congratulates FELEK.

Trading places

NARRATORS: How to describe what happened next day
When people heard of this new ruling—
Some thought it a joke, most thought it unfair,
To make them revisit their schooling.

The adult parliament considered the case:
They were fed up with children who shirk.

So to get their own back, they passed their own law
That said children must turn up for work.

So while adults did sums and played silly games
And tried not to get given lines,
The children discovered it wasn't much fun
In the factories and shops or the mines.

Now, who was more foolish and who was to blame,
It's hard to say with any precision,
But what's not in doubt is how disastrous the
Consequences of a stupid decision!

Machine-tools got broken. The traffic got jammed.
The police were no bigger than you are.
The phones didn't work, the power went out.
Drains blocked and turned street into sewer.

By the end of the week the plight was the same
Across city and village and town.
The country had come to the brink of collapse
And the world had been turned upside-down.

Matt at the station

MATT is wandering his city in disguise, appalled and distressed at the damage. He is at the station. A GUARD wanders past.

MATT: What's happening? Are the trains running?

The GUARD is upset.

GUARD: There's nothing running any more. The old signalman was kept behind for sleeping in class and whoever was supposed to be working the signals . . .

MATT: What is it?

GUARD: I don't know where they went. To play football probably. But they left the damn thing on green. There's been an accident down the track there. Two trains . . .

MATT: Is it bad?

GUARD: Worst I've seen. Some dead. More injured, of course. But heaven knows what state the hospitals are in. Doctors are all in school. Little kid who turned up in the ambulance burst into tears. It's all fallen apart. You'd best go home and see to yourself. That's what I'm doing.

The GUARD exits. MATT stands alone in despair. FELEK enters solemnly. MATT doesn't notice. FELEK hesitates. He whistles. MATT turns round.

MATT: Baron von Rauch.

FELEK: No. Felek. Just plain Felek. I've been looking everywhere for you.

MATT: I've been walking in the city. What's left of it. Have you seen?

FELEK nods.

FELEK: I'm sorry, Matt. It's all my fault. I let things get out of control. I was too busy worrying about titles and limousines.

MATT shakes his head.

MATT: It was me. I wanted to be a Reformer. I thought I could make things better.

FELEK: But you did.

MATT: Doesn't look like it.

FELEK: No. There were lots of good things. It could've worked. It nearly did. We were . . . I mean *I* was just thinking about myself too much.

The JOURNALIST enters with a copy of the newspaper.

JOURNALIST: Well! Majesty, what a surprise. And the noble Baron Von Rauch.

MATT: What are you doing here?

JOURNALIST: Me? I'm just a rat about to leave a sinking ship. But not by train it seems. I must say, wandering through the city, you must be very pleased with your handiwork.

MATT: Pleased? D'you know what I saw? A train crash where people were dying but there was no hospital to take them to 'cause the doctors were all back in the classroom!

The JOURNALIST laughs.

JOURNALIST: Yes. One of my better ideas that.

FELEK suddenly starts to realise.

FELEK: You're right. That was your idea. You were always making suggestions, weren't you. Giving me advice. And I listened. What an idiot I am! You were trying to wreck everything!

JOURNALIST: Me? All I've done is supported you! I didn't pass any laws. You and the children did that all by yourselves.

FELEK: But it was you who told me to send the grown-ups back to school.

JOURNALIST: And it was you who were stupid enough to do it. That's not my fault, is it.

FELEK and MATT close in on the JOURNALIST who reveals his true sneering face.

MATT: You were deliberately trying to sabotage things?

JOURNALIST: I was doing this country a favour! You would've brought it to its knees without any help from me. A boy king? A children's parliament? What a load of old fishwrap! All I did was help restore a bit of order.

FELEK: Order? You call this order?

JOURNALIST: No. I call this chaos. Your chaos. Order arrives tomorrow.

The JOURNALIST shows them the paper.

JOURNALIST: Hot of the press. 'Matt the Brat falls flat.' 'Liberating armies poised to take the capital.'

MATT: What armies?

JOURNALIST: Your old friend the Prince. He crossed your borders about . . . two days ago. Should be here in around . . . twelve hours.

MATT is stunned.

JOURNALIST: Don't look so surprised. You never really thought you could pull it off, did you?

FELEK lunges for the JOURNALIST, but he pulls a gun. FELEK and MATT stand still as the JOURNALIST backs out of the door.

JOURNALIST: I'd start running now if I were you. I don't think the Prince is going to be feeling too merciful when he gets here. Bye bye, King Brat!

The JOURNALIST exits. FELEK goes to follow.

MATT: Leave him, Felek. We have other problems to deal with. I need your help.

FELEK: Anything, sire.

MATT: Their army's only a few miles away. There will only be one battle, on the edge of the city. If we lose, it will be all over.

FELEK can't stand this thought. MATT has an idea.

MATT: Perhaps all is not lost yet. Find the Defence Minister. Tell him what's happening. Tell him to gather whatever is left of the army and form them up on the small hill just outside the city. That's where we'll wait for them. Can you do that?

FELEK: Of course, sire.

MATT: When you're done, I want you to come back and meet me.

FELEK: Here, your Highness?

MATT: No. Meet me at the zoo.

FELEK: The zoo, Highness?

MATT: Yes, the zoo. And Felek . . .

FELEK: Highness?

MATT: Call me Tomek.

FELEK grins. MATT smiles back. They exit.

The final battle

On a hill, outside the city. MATT, FELEK and the MINISTER. A campaign table is set up. The MINISTER is by it, in charge of moving the counters and markers. MATT and FELEK are watching the battlefield below.

NARRATORS: Sometimes in life, all that you do
    Boils down to one single second.
    A turn of a card, a nod of the head,
    And the score is about to be reckoned.

    Matt stood outside his capital
    And knew his time was here.
    No turning back, no other way,
    No time for doubt or fear.

    The morning sun gleamed bright on steel,
    The sky shone pink and red;
    Across the lines of waiting men
    No single word was said.

    And then . . .

    A flare . . .

    The roar of a cannon . . .

    And the charge . . .

The sound of the battle starting as the invaders charge. The MINISTER moves the counters.

MATT: Here they come.

FELEK: D'you think your plan'll work?

MATT: It's possible.

FELEK: But not likely?

MATT: Unlikelier things have happened so far.

FELEK smiles. MATT is watching the battle intently.

MATT: Now wait. Wait. Wait. Ready. And . . . now! Fall back!

MATT signals – an arm movement.

MATT: That's it. Come on, get back out of there.

FELEK: They're slowing. They think we're retreating. Now the surprise.

MATT: Not yet. Let them get closer. More tired. It's a long way to charge uphill.

FELEK: Any minute . . .

MATT: *Now!!*

He waves another signal.

MATT: Now! Open the cages! Open the cages!

The noise of the charge is joined by another noise. Animals.

NARRATORS: The rulebooks of war are ancient and worn,
   Army tactics are hard to disguise,
   But when your men are outnumbered, outgunned and out there,
   That's when you need to spring a surprise.

   Imagine the shock on the face of the troops—
   They must've thought it preposterous—
   When instead of chasing Matt's men up the hill,
   They are running from bears and rhinocerous.

> Lions and tigers and leopards and such
> Are prone to cause people to scatter,
> And to scatter the foe in a battle like this
> Is to scatter the people that matter.

FELEK: Look! They don't know what to do!

MATT: I bet their training didn't cover this.

FELEK: It's working. It's actually working! They're going back.

MATT: Now we drive them back down the hill. Now! Charge!

MATT signals. His men charge. It seems to work.

MATT: They've had enough. We've done it!

They look at each other in astonishment then hug with delight. The MINISTER spots something.

MINISTER: Majesty, wait. Look.

MATT and FELEK look.

MATT: They're coming back. Our men have stopped. What happened?

FELEK: We had it won! We were going to win!!

MINISTER: Sire, above the city, the enemy must've seen it.

MATT looks and can't believe his eyes. Neither can FELEK.

FELEK: A white flag.

MATT: Why have we surrendered?

FELEK: We had them beaten.

MATT: Now we're lost.

The MINISTER folds up the campaign table. The battle is lost.

MATT: They didn't think I could do it. They didn't believe in me. Not any more.

A beat.

MINISTER: What now, your Majesty?

MATT: Now, you leave. Go. Hide. I don't want you caught with me.

FELEK: But . . .

MATT: It's an order, Felek. Go! Save yourselves.

FELEK hesitates.

MATT: Go! Please.

FELEK salutes then leaves with the MINISTER. MATT awaits his fate.

Sentence

The PRINCE faces MATT.

PRINCE: So here we have him, the great King Matt. The Boy Genius. Matt the Reformer. Well, well, well. What do you think of your reforms now? Not so cocky today, are we, boy?

MATT: I'm not a boy. I'm a King. I'm King Matt the First.

The PRINCE glares at him. MATT stares him down.

PRINCE: Matt the First . . . and Last.

The PRINCE gives a signal. A firing squad forms. MATT is stood blindfolded before them.

PRINCE: Ready.

MATT doesn't flinch.

PRINCE: Aim.

A beat.

Afterwards

The firing squad become the narrators. MATT stays where he is.

NARRATORS: So is this the end for our hero, King Matt?
    Does he die all alone in defeat?
    Are there chapters to come about what happens next,
    Or is the story now closed and complete?

    Does Felek come back to Matt's rescue once more
    'Cause he cannot abandon his friend?
    Does the firing squad fail or the Prince change his mind?
    Or is this the ultimate end?

    We could tell you what happens, but then again,
    All we wanted to tell has been told.
    What to make of it now, we will leave up to you
    Let's just hope it's not left you stone cold.

    Was young Matt a fool or an ambitious boy?
    Was he dreaming of personal glory?
    Could his ideas have worked if they'd had half a chance?
    Ah well, that's *your* part of the story . . .

And so there was a boy.

And so there was a King.

And so that was what happened.

End

The Life of Stuff

Simon Donald

Sex, drugs and Frank Sinatra: The Life of Stuff is a brilliantly funny fly-on-the-wall snapshot of eight lives careering out of control as small-time crook and aspirant pharmaceutical entrepreneur Willie Dobie's best laid plans unravel when human nature takes its predictably unpredictable course... In common with a number of first-rate modern Scottish plays The Life of Stuff has, as yet, only received two professional productions. I fervently hope this new publication will lead to the wider recognition it deserves.

Hugh Hodgart, Head of Acting at RSAMD, Glasgow

Furiously contemporary, extremely funny and has a cast of outrageous yet sympathetic characters which take possession like a cult.

Julie Morrice, Scotland on Sunday

ISBN 0-9545206-6-1

£5.99

Available from Booksource Tel: 0870 240 2182
and www.capercailliebooks.co.uk

The Waltzer

Rhiannon Tise

The Waltzer is a touching and sensitive exploration of the serious business of growing up. A world of beleaguered single parents and adolescent fears and friendships is reflected in the dark mirror of Sally's experience on her first real date. The garish glamour and hectic motion of the fairground and the Waltzer itself provide a perfect setting for this multi-faceted depiction of the thrills and spills of a teenager's first steps towards the adult world. Written for radio, The Waltzer draws much of its power and point from the complex interaction between past and present events, inner monologue and intercut dialogue. In our film and TV dominated culture we can easily miss out on the imaginative strength of radio drama – the publication of this play is a timely reminder of the real alternatives to the siren call of MTV, Cartoon Network and the Disney Channel.

Hugh Hodgart, Head of Acting at RSAMD, Glasgow

ISBN 0-9545206-3-7

£5.99

Available from Booksource Tel: 0870 240 2182
and www.capercailliebooks.co.uk

Dr Korczak's Example

David Greig

Dr Korczak's Example is set in the final, numbered, days of an orphanage in the Warsaw ghetto in 1942. Based on real events, this 'Brechtian' retelling generates an almost unbearable power and pathos through the simple humanity, warts and all, of the central characters who are trapped both by the inexorable forces of Nazi oppression and by our fore-knowledge of the fate that awaits them. The play's 'alienation' device of depicting its characters through the use of dolls, further enhances our painful feeling of powerlessness. Yet, in spite of its tragic outcome, Dr Korczak's Example, like the real life of its protagonist, leaves us exhilarated and uplifted by the indomitable power of love.

Hugh Hodgart, Head of Acting at RSAMD, Glasgow

This is the dramatist's art turned to serve an idea of theatre which is unreproducable in any other medium – a play not to forget.

Will Hutton, The Observer

ISBN 0-9545206-1-0

£5.99

Available from Booksource Tel: 0870 240 2182
and www.capercailliebooks.co.uk

Kaahini

Maya Chowdhry

Kaahini is a highly original yet thoroughly accessible insight into what it means to be young, Asian and British. Filled with the powerful and contradictory emotions of adolescence, Kaahini is brightly coloured, full of warmth and feeling, and shot through with the darker threads of frustration and anger at the inflexible and inexplicable adult world. This play, for all its seemingly unfamiliar Asian context, speaks directly to the widest possible audience: anyone with a mother, father, son, daughter, friend or lover will find much to challenge and inspire them here.

Hugh Hodgart, Head of Acting at RSAMD, Glasgow

Maya Chowdhry's Kaahini is a surprising, tender and beautifully observed play, which manages the elusive feat of exploring gender and cultural politics in a thought-provoking way without ever distracting from the passionate heart of its story. A play which deserves to be seen by as many young people as possible.

John E McGrath, Artistic Director, Contact, Manchester

ISBN 0-9545206-4-5

£5.99

Available from Booksource Tel: 0870 240 2182
and www.capercailliebooks.co.uk

Sunburst Finish

Andrea Gibb
Paddy Cunneen

'Note to self. You are dying.' As a young man's depression turns to despair, suicide seems the only way out - the only way to take control. In spite of the bleakness of its subject, *Sunburst Finish* is filled with strong and vibrant voices, a rich mosaic of music, wit, warmth, insight, feeling, and a remarkable lack of sentimentality. The central character's struggle to come to terms with himself and the world around him is one that all young (and not so young) people will relate strongly to.

Hugh Hodgart, Head of Acting at RSAMD, Glasgow

ISBN 0-9545206-5-3

£5.99

Available from Booksource Tel: 0870 240 2182
and www.capercailliebooks.co.uk

Shakespeare The Director's Cut

Michael Bogdanov

This collection of cutting-edge essays is a valuable addition to Shakespeare studies, and to theatre studies more generally. Michael Bogdanov's cuts are always incisive, razor-sharp, and applied with an unerring hand. Never dogmatic or programmatic, Bogdanov approaches each play attentive to its novelty and its nuances, alive to its urgency and impact, attuned to its language and its lore. As a director acutely aware of critical conventions – enough to want to overturn them – Bogdanov is uniquely positioned to combine theoretical acuity with a practitioner's knowledge of what works on the page and in performance, while never losing sight of what is most politically resonant and socially engaged. The meat is moist closest to the bone, and these are choice cuts from a master butcher.

Willy Maley, Professor of Renaissance Studies,

University of Glasgow

For 30 years Michael Bogdanov has been the most consistently interesting and provocative of British directors of Shakespeare. Now he has written a series of incisive essays on the plays – not comments on his many productions, but introductions to the works that show the result of his long acquaintance with them. The essays, based in social thought and theatrical savvy, make Shakespeare accessible and immediate and will be of interest to a wide range of readers.

Dennis Kennedy, Beckett Professor of Drama,

Trinity College Dublin

Michael Bogdanov is the Tyrone Guthrie of our day, and his signature is all over the work of many young directors. He is at once scholar, provocateur, puritan and Lord of Misrule.

Michael Pennington

ISBN 0-9545206-0-2

£8.99

Available from Booksource Tel: 0870 240 2182
and www.capercailliebooks.co.uk
From all major bookshops and www.amazon.co.uk